NO IS NO
SÍ IS YES

KUMQUAT

Queda hecho el depósito que previene la Ley 11.723

Diseño Andrés Sobrino

Ediciones Kumquat, Buenos Aires, Argentina
Email: kumquat@kumquat.com.ar
www.kumquatediciones.com
Impreso en Latin Gráfica, Buenos Aires, Argentina.
Primera edición, mayo 2005
ISBN 987-21791-8-2

Galán, Ana.
No es no : sí es yes / Ana Galan ; ilustrado por Daniel Chaskielberg.
- 1a ed. – Buenos Aires : Kumquat, 2005.
32 p. : il. ; 20x20 cm.

ISBN 987-21791-8-2

1. Inglés-Rimas. 2. Español-Rimas. I. Chaskielberg, Daniel, ilus. II. Título
CDD 811 : 861

BY ANA GALAN

ILLUSTRATED BY DANIEL CHASKIELBERG

EDITED BY ALEJANDRA LONGO

1
NO

No is no, sí is yes;
one, two, three is
uno, dos, tres.

HANDS

Hands are manos.
Feet are pies.
Arms are brazos;
piernas: legs.

LEGS

ARMS
FEET

Car is carro.
Tren is train.
Boat is barco.
Avión is plane.

TAXI

UP

Up is arriba.
Down is abajo.
Side by side,
de lado a lado.

SIDE BY SIDE

ABAJO

ARRIBA

DE LADO A LADO

DOWN

DOG
PE
PATO
CABALLO

CAT
GATO
DUCK
Dog is perro.
Cat is gato.
Horse, caballo.
Duck is pato.
HORSE

WHITE
BLANCO
BLACK
NEGRO

Black is negro.
White is blanco.
Red is rojo.
Purple, morado.

PURPLE
MORADO

RED
ROJO

Fat is gordo.
Thin is flaco.
Short is bajo.
Tall is alto.

SHORT
TALL

CALIENTE HOT

RÍO

RIVER

Hot is caliente.
Cold is frío.

COLD
FRÍO
SEA
Sea is el mar.
River is río.

HAPPY

CONTENTO

Happy is **contento.**
Tired is **cansado.**
Hungry is **hambriento.**
Angry is **enfadado.**

TIRED

CANSADO

HUNGRY

HAMBRIENTO

ANGRY

ENFADADO

DAD
PAPÁ
MOM
MAMÁ

Dad is papá.
Uncle is tío.
Mom is mamá.
Cousin is primo.

¿CÓMO
HOW ARE ST
LE VEO DESPUÉS

How are you?
¿Cómo está usted?
See you later:
le veo después.

Tú eres mi amigo is
you are my friend.
Dilo otra vez
is say it again.

MI AMIGO

MY FRIEND

DILO OTRA VEZ
SAY IT AGAIN

WHAT?
WHY?
¿POR QUÉ?

¿QUÉ?

What? is **¿qué?**
Why?, **¿por qué?**
I don't know
is **no lo sé.**

I DON'T KNOW

NO LO SÉ

Now say fin

and that's the end.

FIN

EL FIN
THE END
TAXI